CGP is your fictional friend for the SATs!

This brilliant SAT Buster from CGP is bursting with practice to help pupils build their fiction reading skills for the KS2 English SATs!

There's a huge variety of interesting fiction texts, each with questions covering the specific reading skills they'll be tested on.

We've even included a handy scoresheet at the back to keep track of how much progress they've made. Amazing!

What CGP is all about

Our sole aim here at CGP is to produce the highest quality books — carefully written, immaculately presented and dangerously close to being funny.

Then we work our socks off to get them out to you — at the cheapest possible prices.

Contents

Section 1 – The Baking Battle

Section 3 – The Old Photograph

Section 2 – An Underground City

Section 4 – A Visit to Baba Yaga

Published by CGP

Editors: Izzy Bowen, Tom Carney, Emma Crighton, Kelsey Hammond, Catherine Heygate, Holly Robinson, Sean Walsh

ISBN: 978 1 78294 830 8

With thanks to Glenn Rogers for the proofreading.

Printed by Elanders Ltd, Newcastle upon Tyne.
Clipart from Corel®

Based on the classic CGP style created by Richard Parsons.

Here's what you have to do:

In Year 6 you have to take some tests called the SATs.
This book will help you do well in the reading bit of the tests.

The reading paper will test you on eight different reading elements:

2a Word Meanings   **2c** Summarising   **2e** Predictions   **2g** Language

2b Fact Retrieval   **2d** Inferences   **2f** Structure   **2h** Comparisons

These elements are used to see how well you can understand texts.

To help you improve your reading skills, this book has separate question pages for each of the reading elements — so you always know which one you are practising.

This is a Tellastaurius — it can read and understand even the trickiest fiction texts.

Your aim is to become a Tellastaurius.

Work through the questions in the book. When you finish a section, add up your marks and write them in the scoresheet at the end of the book.

Then, put a tick in the box at the end of the section to show how you got on.   →   

  If you got a lot of questions wrong, put a tick in the circle on the left. Don't worry — every Tellastaurius has to start somewhere. Read the texts again carefully, then have another go.

If you're nearly there but you're still a bit wobbly on some questions, put a tick in the middle circle. Ask your teacher to help you work out the areas you need more practice on.

 If you felt really confident and got nearly all the answers right, tick the circle on the right.

Congratulations — you're a Tellastaurius!

The Baking Battle

This story is about a school baking competition, and what can happen when two people who really don't like each other are put together in a team. There are some surprising results!

What to do

1) Open out the folding pages, and read the story *The Baking Battle*.

2) After that, shake out your arms and legs — wave each arm around in the air, then give each leg a good wiggle. Now read the story again.

3) Once that's done, move on to answering the questions.

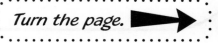 *Turn the page.*

Fact Retrieval Questions

6) Read the paragraph beginning **'Demi and Jack glanced...'**
Give **one** task that Demi was good at.

....

1 mark

7) Look again at the paragraph which starts **'Demi and Jack glanced...'**
Who did Demi and Jack expect to win the competition?

....

1 mark

8) Write down **two** things you are told about what the winners' medals look like.

....

....

2 marks

9) What did Demi and Jack do with their cake after the competition finished?

....

1 mark

10) Use the information from the text to match up the actions with who did them.
One has been done for you.

whisked the batter   just Jack

put the cake in the oven   Alison and Tyrone

tidied up the table   Mrs Fenton

won the competition   Demi and Jack

2 marks

Tellastauriuses can retrieve facts with the swish of a tail. Can you? Tick to show how these pages went.

© CGP — not to be photocopied

Section 1 — The Baking Battle

Inference Questions

INFERENCE questions ask you to work out what's going on in the text when the writer hasn't told you directly. Have another read of the text, then have a go at these questions.

1) **'Demi's heart sank. Jack's face fell.'**

What does this tell you about how Demi and Jack felt about being put in a team together?

....

1 mark

2) **'Working with Jack was a nightmare...'**
Is this a fact or an opinion?

> A fact can be proved. An opinion is what someone thinks — it can't be proved.

....

1 mark

3) Look at the part of the text that starts **'Jack jostled Demi...'** and ends **'...break the eggs.'''**

a) In this section, Demi seems

happy	competitive	lazy	scared

Circle your answer.

1 mark

b) In this section, Jack seems

lonely	cheerful	noisy	bossy

Circle your answer.

1 mark

4) Look at page 4.

Find and copy a phrase that suggests Demi didn't want to crack the eggs.

....

1 mark

| 2d | **Inference Questions** |

5) Find and copy a phrase that shows Jack's technique for cracking the eggs worked for Demi.

....

———
1 mark

6) Look at page 5.

How can you tell that Demi and Jack were worried they were running out of time?

....

———
1 mark

7) Read the last paragraph.

How do you think Demi and Jack felt in this paragraph?

Use evidence from the text to support your answer.

> You can use 'because' to link your answer to your evidence.

....

....

———
2 marks

8) The end of the text says that Demi and Jack made **'a pretty great cake — and an even better team.'**

What other evidence is there in the text that they made a good team?

Give **two** things.

....

....

....

———
2 marks

Tellastauriuses find inference questions as easy as catching their dinner. How about you?

Word Meaning Questions

WORD MEANING questions are just what they say on the tin — they ask you about what a word from the text means. If you don't know a word, read the rest of the sentence for clues.

1) **'Having glanced through the recipe, Demi dived for the flour...'**
   What does the word **'glanced'** mean in this sentence?

   | blinked | glared | looked | thought |

   Circle your answer.

   _____
   1 mark

2) **'As she attempted to fish fragments of shell out of the bowl...'**
   Which word in this sentence tells you that the egg had broken into pieces?

   ....
   _____
   1 mark

3) **'Together they hoisted the flour up to the scales.'**
   What does the word **'hoisted'** mean in this sentence? Tick **one** box.

   threw [ ]

   sieved [ ]

   weighed [ ]

   lifted [ ]

   _____
   1 mark

4) **'...clutching two gold medals in her hand.'**
   What does the word **'clutching'** mean in this sentence?

   ....
   _____
   1 mark

Tellastauriuses know the meanings of even the trickiest words. How did you find this page?

2c   Summary Questions

Answering SUMMARY questions means thinking about what the text means overall, or how you might summarise a chunk of it. Try these questions out for size.

1) Look at the part of the text that starts **'Everyone sprang into action...'** and ends **'...heavy bag of flour.'**

Which sentence best summarises this section? Tick **one** box.

Demi and Jack's cake-making starts off smoothly. ☐

Demi and Jack's cake-making starts off badly. ☐

Demi doesn't know Jack very well. ☐

Jack knocks over the flour. ☐

1 mark

2) What is the main message of the story?

| Teachers shouldn't bake cakes. | It's better to work together. | It's better to do things alone. | Winning is important. |

Circle your answer.

1 mark

2f   Structure Question

STRUCTURE questions are all about what comes when in the text, and why. Read the text again, then have a go at this question about the structure of 'The Baking Battle'.

1) Find and copy the sentence where Demi and Jack's attitudes towards each other changed.

....

....

1 mark

Tellastauriuses are great at answering summary and structure questions. How about you?

An Underground City

World War Two, which took place between 1939 and 1945, made life in the UK very difficult. In this story, three children visit a museum about old air-raid shelters, where people used to go to find safety during the war. As you read the story, try to imagine what it was like for people who had to stay in the shelters.

What to do

1) Open out the folding pages, and read the story *An Underground City*.

2) When you've done that, whisper 'Alakazam!' — for a bit of magic luck — then read it again.

3) When you've read it for a second time, make a start on the questions.

Turn the page. ➡

Fact Retrieval Questions

6) Read the paragraph beginning **'The sight confirmed...'**
Which of the following facts can be found in this part of the text? Tick **one** box.

The air-raid shelters were only for rich people. ☐

The air-raid shelters were only for people visiting the area. ☐

The air-raid shelters were used to escape bombing. ☐

The air-raid shelters were used during World War One. ☐

1 mark

7) Read the paragraph beginning **'The three wandered along...'**
Complete the table with the evidence that helped Nathan, Tia and Umar identify each room. One has been done for you.

Room	Evidence
medical room	old equipment
post office	
kitchen	

2 marks

8) Who reminded everyone of the time?

....

1 mark

9) Why did Nathan, Tia and Umar want to visit the museum?
Explain your answer fully.

....

....

....

2 marks

Tellastauriuses can pick out information from the trickiest of texts. How did you get on?

Inference Questions

To answer INFERENCE questions, you need to put on your thinking cap and work out what's really going on in the story. Have another read through, then have a go at these questions.

1) How can you tell the group were bored when they were travelling to the museum?

....

1 mark

2) Read the paragraph beginning **'Finally they emerged...'**
   Find and copy a phrase that suggests the first tunnel the group entered was long.

....

1 mark

3) Read the paragraph beginning **'Deciding to venture further...'**
   How can you tell from this paragraph that the square chamber was uncomfortable to stay in?

....

1 mark

4) a) Look at page 14. At first, Umar thought the idea of sleeping underground was

   | exciting | upsetting | scary | boring |

   Circle your answer.

1 mark

   b) Explain your answer, making sure you refer to the text.

....

....

1 mark

5) Why did Nathan describe the shelters as **'like an underground city'**?

....

....

1 mark

Inference Questions

2d

6) **'"Now we're really going to have to stay the night," said Umar.'**
Why did this make Nathan think about the bunk beds?

....

....
_____
1 mark

7) Read from **'Suddenly, a voice called out...'** to **'...I found you so quickly."'**
How did Amanda feel about the group in this part of the text?
Explain your answer using evidence from the text.

Think about how Amanda speaks and acts.

....

....
_____
2 marks

8) Find and copy a phrase that tells you Nathan, Tia and Umar wrote a lot for their project.

....
_____
1 mark

9) Using each option once, match each of the events from the story with an emotion you think Nathan was feeling. One has been done for you.

Nathan's dad suggests a different activity.   **amazement**

Nathan sees the door to the tunnels.   **fear**

Nathan enters the tunnels.   **excitement**

Nathan realises they are lost.   **disappointment** _____

2 marks

Inference questions are easy peasy for a Tellastaurius. How did you find these pages?

Word Meaning Questions

WORD MEANING questions test whether you've understood the different words in the text — it's a chance to show off your vocabulary. Look back at the text and try these questions.

1) Read the paragraph beginning '**"Never mind," Nathan's dad said...**'
Which word in this paragraph tells you that the door was slightly open?

....

_____
1 mark

2) '**...he was completely absorbed by the old photos.**'
Circle the word which means the same as '**absorbed**' in this sentence.

| hurt | overjoyed | fascinated | confused |

_____
1 mark

3) '**They began to move, then froze.**'
What does the word '**froze**' mean in this sentence?

....

_____
1 mark

4) Read the paragraph beginning '**Amanda frowned...**'
Which word in this paragraph could be replaced by the word 'worried'?

....

_____
1 mark

5) Read the paragraph beginning '**"We needed information," Nathan blurted out...**'
What does the word '**eager**' mean in this paragraph? Tick **one** box.

late ☐   surprised ☐

afraid ☐   keen ☐

Try replacing 'eager' with each option — only one will keep the meaning the same.

_____
1 mark

Word meaning questions are a piece of cake for Tellastauriuses. How did you get on with them?

⋮ *The last few questions on <u>An Underground City</u> are under here.* ➡ ⋮

"We were," his dad confirmed. "We toured all over Europe — five shows a week, every week. We were the stars of the show."

Jackson was dumbfounded. "Why did you stop?" he croaked.

"Life on the road just got a bit tiring for us after a while," his father explained. "Fifteen years ago, we packed everything up, and we haven't looked back since."

Jackson's eyes were still glued in astonishment to the batons before him.

"Want to see?" his father asked, jumping up. He called out to Jackson's mother, who laughed with surprise when she saw the relics sitting in her husband's hands. The dynamic duo began throwing the clubs across the garage to each other, starting cautiously but rapidly speeding up until there was nothing but a blur of colour in the air between them. Their hands seemed to move at an inexplicable speed as they tossed the clubs in increasingly complex combinations.

As each club ascended higher and higher towards the garage ceiling, apparently unaffected by gravity, Jackson could imagine the delight on the spectators' faces in years gone by. He could almost hear the roar of the crowd as his parents stunned them with their incredible tricks.

Eventually one club dropped to the floor with a clatter.

"Like riding a bike," Jackson's father laughed. "Almost."

"Can I try?" pleaded Jackson.

After an afternoon spent learning the basics of juggling with his parents, Jackson couldn't believe he'd ever been reluctant to tidy the garage. He'd unveiled a surprising and inspiring story, and as he returned the juggling clubs to their box that evening, he couldn't help hoping that he might one day amaze an audience with all kinds of astonishing and breathtaking juggling tricks — just like his parents had done all those years ago.

← *Open the flap for the start of the story.*

Section 3 — The Old Photograph

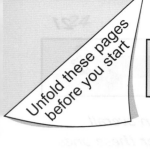

2b   Fact Retrieval Questions

For each FACT RETRIEVAL question, you need to look through the text, spot the information, then answer the question. See how you do with these.

1) What did Jackson's dad agree to do in exchange for Jackson's help tidying the garage?

....

1 mark

2) a) What reason did Jackson's dad give for wanting to tidy the garage?

....

1 mark

b) According to Jackson, what was the real reason his dad wanted to tidy the garage?

....

1 mark

3) At what time of day did Jackson and his dad tidy the garage?

| morning | afternoon | evening | night |

Circle your answer.

1 mark

4) Why did Jackson finish tidying the last two boxes on his own?

....

1 mark

5) Which items did Jackson find in the same box as the photograph?
Tick **two** boxes.

a comic book   ☐

some puzzle games   ☐

a turquoise suit   ☐

a piggy bank   ☐

a set of juggling clubs   ☐

2 marks

Fact Retrieval Questions

2b

6) Give **two** things you are told about the father's appearance in the photograph.

....

....

2 marks

7) Where did the circus travel?

....

1 mark

8) Why did Jackson's parents leave the circus?

| They got too old. | They found juggling tiring. | They found travelling tiring. | They had a baby. |

Circle your answer.

1 mark

9) How did Jackson's mother react when she first saw the juggling clubs?

....

1 mark

10) Write down **one** thing that Jackson imagined seeing and **one** thing he imagined hearing when his parents were juggling in the garage.

Seeing: ....

Hearing: ....

2 marks

Tellastauriuses can do fact retrieval questions whilst dancing at the 'Dino Disco'. How about you?

Section 3 — The Old Photograph

Inference Questions

INFERENCE questions get you to dig a bit deeper, so they can seem quite tricky — but if you think carefully about what's going on in the story, you should find the answer. Try these ones.

1) Read the first paragraph.

How did Jackson feel about the agreement? Tick **one** box.

He was angry about it. ☐

He was satisfied with it. ☐

He didn't care about it. ☐

He was sad about it. ☐

1 mark

2) **'Jackson had rolled his eyes every time his dad had asked him to tidy the garage.'**

How does this suggest Jackson felt about being asked to tidy the garage?

....

....

1 mark

3) Read the paragraph beginning **'In the garage...'**

How can you tell from this paragraph that nothing had been touched in the garage for a long time?

....

1 mark

4) Read the paragraph beginning **'When the dust had settled...'**

Who are the **'lines of eager eyes'**?

....

1 mark

2d

Inference Questions

5) Read the paragraph that starts **'They were in...'**
   Give **one** detail in this paragraph that suggests the juggling clubs are old.

   ....

   1 mark

6) Look again at the paragraph beginning **'They were in...'**
   Find and copy a phrase from this paragraph that suggests Jackson's dad is good at juggling.

   ....

   1 mark

7) Read the paragraph beginning **'"Want to see?" his father asked...'**
   How does this paragraph make Jackson's parents' juggling seem impressive?

   ....

   ....

   ....

   2 marks

8) **'He'd unveiled a surprising and inspiring story...'**
   Why was the story of his parents' past both
   'surprising' and **'inspiring'** for Jackson?

   > Make sure you explain why Jackson was both surprised and inspired.

   ....

   ....

   ....

   2 marks

Tellastauriuses can answer inference questions faster than lightning. How about you?

Word Meaning Questions

Words, words, words... they're everywhere, and you need to be able to say what they mean.
Read 'The Old Photograph' again and then get down to answering these questions.

1) **'They had been hammering out the details of a complex negotiation...'**
   What does the word **'complex'** mean in this sentence? Tick **one** box.

   complicated ☐   simple ☐

   furious ☐   long ☐

   _____
   1 mark

2) Look at the paragraph beginning **'Eventually, his father offered...'**
   What does the word **'hefty'** tell you about the pile of rubbish?

   ....
   _____
   1 mark

3) Look at the paragraph beginning **'Setting the juice down...'**
   Which word in this paragraph tells you that Jackson's dad moved quickly?

   ....
   _____
   1 mark

4) **'...Jackson could see several unsightly cracks...'**
   Circle the word that could replace the word **'unsightly'** in this sentence.

   | unclear | | invisible | | unusual | | ugly |

   _____
   1 mark

5) Find and copy **one** word from page 25 that suggests Jackson was desperate
   to try juggling.

   ....
   _____
   1 mark

Tellastauriuses can do word meaning questions
with their eyes closed. How did you find them?

The last few questions on <u>*The Old Photograph*</u> *are under here.* ➡

"Are you still weaving, my pretty?" croaked Baba Yaga.
"Yes, Baba Yaga!" trilled the cat, trying its best to mimic Natasha's voice.

"That's not my supper!" roared Baba Yaga, storming in. When she spotted the cat at the loom, she let out a deafening shriek.

"You flea-infested traitor! Where is the girl? Why didn't you scratch her eyes out when she tried to escape?"

The cat jabbed its paw in Baba Yaga's direction. "You let me starve, but that girl gave me her last bite of food. That's why I let her go."

Baba Yaga threw the cat a poisonous glare and charged out of the hut, heading straight for the dog.

"You foul mongrel! Why didn't you bite the girl as she escaped?"

The dog levelled a hard stare at Baba Yaga. "You make me hunt all day for something to eat. She gave me delicious bread."

Baba Yaga gnashed her iron teeth, and flew to the gate, delivering it a swift kick.

"Why didn't you squeak and alert me to her escape?"

The gate clanged shut angrily. "Not once have you oiled my rusting hinges, yet that girl took the time to tend to my aching joints. I've never felt less like squeaking in my entire life!"

Baba Yaga clenched her bony fists and let out a ghastly howl that echoed through the air.

Natasha raced through the woods until the familiar sight of her cabin came into view. Relief flooded her body as she saw her father chopping wood outside. She barrelled into him and hugged him tightly, breathing in the sweet scent of sap and wood smoke on his shirt.

"Darling Natasha, where have you been?" he asked, stroking her hair.

Natasha explained how her stepmother had sent her to Baba Yaga's hut, and how she had come perilously close to finding herself on Baba Yaga's dinner plate. Her father hugged her closer, a tear rolling down his face.

The next morning, Natasha noticed that all of her stepmother's possessions had vanished from the cabin. Through the window, she saw a trail of slender footprints in the mud outside, heading away from their cabin and towards the city far in the distance.

Open the flap for the start of the story.

Section 4 — A Visit to Baba Yaga

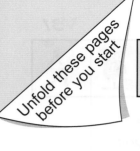

2b **Fact Retrieval Questions** 🐕

Answering FACT RETRIEVAL questions is like a treasure hunt — but instead of gold, you're hunting for nuggets of information that are buried in the text.

1) At the beginning of the story, how long had Natasha and her stepmother lived together for?

two days	two weeks	two months	two years

Circle your answer.

_____
1 mark

2) What did Natasha's stepmother want to borrow from Baba Yaga?

....
_____
1 mark

3) What are Baba Yaga's teeth made of?

....
_____
1 mark

4) Write down **two** things that Natasha took with her to Baba Yaga's hut.

....

....
_____
2 marks

5) Why did Natasha put oil on the gate's hinges?

....
_____
1 mark

6) Read the paragraph beginning **'Beyond the gate...'**
Write down **two** things you are told about the chimney of Baba Yaga's hut.

....

....
_____
2 marks

2b Fact Retrieval Questions

7) Look at page 34.
    Natasha approached Baba Yaga's house

| noisily | quietly | angrily | cheerfully |

Circle your answer.

_____
1 mark

8) What was Baba Yaga doing when Natasha arrived?

....
_____
1 mark

9) Where was Baba Yaga's cat when Natasha first saw it?

....
_____
1 mark

10) How did Baba Yaga's cat help Natasha to escape?

....

....
_____
1 mark

11) Why didn't Baba Yaga's dog stop Natasha from escaping?

....

....
_____
1 mark

A Tellastaurius would have no trouble answering these fact retrieval questions. How did you get on?

Inference Questions

To answer INFERENCE questions, you have to dig a bit deeper into the meaning of the text. So make sure you've got your spade handy before you tackle the next couple of pages.

1) Find and copy a phrase from page 33 which suggests that the forest near Natasha's cabin might be dangerous.

....

_____
1 mark

2) Read the paragraph that starts **'Although her stepmother had only...'**
What evidence is there that Natasha's stepmother is unkind?

....

....

....

_____
2 marks

3) a) **'...Natasha felt her blood turn to ice.'**
What feeling do you think Natasha was experiencing here?

....

_____
1 mark

b) Why do you think Natasha felt this way?

....

....

_____
1 mark

4) **'"That's not my supper!" roared Baba Yaga...'**
Why did Baba Yaga shout this?

....

....

_____
1 mark

2d　　　　**Inference Questions**

5) How can you tell that Baba Yaga was angry at the cat for letting
Natasha escape?

....

....

....
　　　　　　　　　　　　　　　　　　　　　　　　　　　　　　　　—————
　　　　　　　　　　　　　　　　　　　　　　　　　　　　　　　　2 marks

6) a) Which of these adjectives best describes Natasha? Circle **one**.

| caring | rude | cunning | selfish |

　　　　　　　　　　　　　　　　　　　　　　　　　　　　　　　　—————
　　　　　　　　　　　　　　　　　　　　　　　　　　　　　　　　1 mark

b) Use information from the text to explain your answer.

....

....

....
　　　　　　　　　　　　　　　　　　　　　　　　　　　　　　　　—————
　　　　　　　　　　　　　　　　　　　　　　　　　　　　　　　　2 marks

7) **'Her father hugged her closer, a tear rolling down his face.'**
Why do you think Natasha's father was crying?

> Try to explain your
> answer fully by referring
> to evidence in the text.

....

....

....
　　　　　　　　　　　　　　　　　　　　　　　　　　　　　　　　—————
　　　　　　　　　　　　　　　　　　　　　　　　　　　　　　　　2 marks

*Tellastauriuses can make inferences while jumping
like a jelly bean. Can you? Give yourself a tick.*

Word Meaning Questions

There can be some really tricky words in WORD MEANING questions. If you're not sure what a word means, look at the sentence as a whole for clues to help you work it out.

1) Baba Yaga feasted on **'any children unfortunate enough to cross her path'**.
   What does the word **'unfortunate'** mean in this sentence?

   ....

   _____
   1 mark

2) **'...Baba Yaga will be delighted to see you...'**
   Which word could the writer have used instead of **'delighted'** in this sentence?

   | disappointed | determined | furious | pleased |

   Circle your answer.

   _____
   1 mark

3) **'...her iron teeth glinting in a sinister smile.'**
   Which of the words below is closest in meaning to the word **'sinister'**?

   | friendly | threatening | ugly | cheerful |

   Circle your answer.

   _____
   1 mark

4) **'Natasha nodded hastily...'**
   What does the word **'hastily'** mean in this sentence?

   ....

   _____
   1 mark

5) Look at the paragraph beginning **'The next morning...'**
   Find and copy a word from this paragraph that means 'narrow'.

   ....

   _____
   1 mark

Tellastauriuses can answer word meaning questions with their claws tied behind their backs. Can you?

Summary Question

SUMMARY questions ask you to bring together information from across the text — so it wouldn't hurt to read 'A Visit to Baba Yaga' again before answering this question...

1) a) Tick the option which is a main idea of the text.

Baba Yaga is kind to animals. ☐

Cats are untrustworthy. ☐

Baba Yaga is cruel. ☐

Natasha loves her stepmother. ☐

Think about how these characters are described in the text.

1 mark

b) Explain how this is shown in the text.

....

....

....

2 marks

Language Question

Writers sometimes choose fancier words than usual to make their stories more interesting — LANGUAGE questions are about these words and why they're used. Give this one a go.

1) **'The dog sniffed it cautiously, then snapped it up eagerly.'**

Why do you think the writer chose the words **'snapped'** and **'eagerly'** here?

....

....

1 mark

Tellastauriuses can summarise thirty things before breakfast, and they love fancy words. How about you?

Scoresheet

Great work, you're all finished with this book. Use the answer book to find out how well you did and write your marks in the table below.

	Section 1 – The Baking Battle	Section 2 – An Underground City	Section 3 – The Old Photograph	Section 4 – A Visit to Baba Yaga	Total
2a Word Meanings	/ 4	/ 5	/ 5	/ 5	/ 19
2b Fact Retrieval	/ 13	/ 11	/ 14	/ 13	/ 51
2c Summarising	/ 2	/ 2	/ 2	/ 3	/ 9
2d Inferences	/ 11	/ 12	/ 10	/ 13	/ 46
2e Predictions		/ 2			/ 2
2f Structure	/ 1				/ 1
2g Language				/ 1	/ 1
2h Comparisons			/ 1		/ 1
Total	/ 31	/ 32	/ 32	/ 35	/ 130

Look at your total score to see how you're doing and where you need more practice:

0 – 60 — Don't worry if you got lots wrong. Revise the reading skills you're struggling with and then have another go at the questions.

61 – 110 — You're doing well. Look back at any reading elements you're struggling with and try the questions again to make sure you're happy with them.

111 – 130 — Good work, you're doing great. Give yourself a pat on the back.